Dreamcatcher
AND THE SEVEN DECEIVERS

Asabikeshiiwasp
GAYE AWIYA OGA-GAGWE-NIISIBIDOON

David Bouchard
PAINTINGS BY **Kristy Cameron**
MUSIC BY **Stephen Kakfwi**
OJIBWE LANGUAGE BY **Jason** AND **Nancy Jones**

MORE THAN WORDS
MTW
PUBLISHERS

A WORD FROM THE AUTHOR

The Sun, the Moon and the Earth ...
Giizis, Dibikigiizis gaye Gidakiiminaan ...

The Medicine Wheel, the Round Dance
and the *Dreamcatcher* ...

All circles – *all circles of life*.

What goes up will come down. What
you give away will always come back
to you. In all things, there is balance.
For every right, there is a wrong.
For each of the Sacred Teachings,
there is a Deceiver.

At a time before distant religions and
churches came with their teachings,
their commandments and their seven
cardinal sins, we knew.

We knew the way of the Good Red Road.

We knew the right way to live; not
through commandments but through
Sacred Teachings – Teachings that were
given to us long before their arrival.

And we knew we would be tested by
Seven Deceivers – what they called
seven cardinal sins.

We knew because we had been
forewarned.

And when these distant churches
arrived on Turtle Island (North America)
with their teachings, their relics
and their symbols, we had our own.
One was the *Dreamcatcher*.

Sometimes, Breath Giver comes to us
directly, as he did with the Teachings
of White Buffalo Calf Woman. On other
occasions, Creator sends for us, as
he did when we were brought before
the Seven Grandfathers. More often,
however, Creator sends Trickster to
guide and help us find our way along
the Good Red Road. And though Creator
has given us the freedom to make our
own choices in life, he intervenes when
necessary ... but only when necessary ...
during a time of great crisis and need.

It was during such a time that we were
gifted the Sacred Pipe. It was during a
time of great need that we were taught
how to build and use the Sweat Lodge.
The Great Flood occurred at such
a time and it was during a time of
crisis and great need that our guide,
the Trickster, came and gifted us with
the *Dreamcatcher*.

Dreamcatcher and the Seven Deceivers
ASABIKESHIIWASP GAYE AWIYA OGA-GAGWE-NIISIBIDOON

Long before our Grandmothers were young, greed, corruption and malice had taken hold of Turtle Island.

It was at this time that an Anishinabek youth began the fourth day of his Vision Quest.

As custom dictates, this young man had little with him: a robe to fight off the cold; tobacco for offering; sweetgrass and sage for purifying and cleansing.

Pure of mind and heart, the youth sat on the bank of a dried out creek crying for a vision. His eyes were closed and his heart was open. An onlooker might have thought him alone but he was not. Trickster was there next to him … whispering in his ear.

The boy stood and began scanning the blanket of Mother Earth. He picked up a long, green twig and shaped it into a circle. Using a strip of leather from his moccasin, he tied then hung the hoop on a branch of a small sage bush.

He then watched Grandmother Spider step out of the tall grass and begin climbing the hoop. With ease and grace, she made her way to the top. From there, she spoke to him.

Gichi-mewinzha Kokomisinaanig gii-oshki-aya'aawiwaad, niibowa gegoo gii-mashizhidoodaadiwag ondenigewin gaye o'omaa mikinaakominising.

Aazha ogii-kikendaan gaa-izhichiged, bangii eta gegoo odayaan: waaboowaan ge-onji-giizhoosid, asemaan waa-piindaakoojigaaded: wiinbashk gaye nookwezigan ge-onji-bagaki-naanaagadawendang.

Ezhi-onabid jiigi-baade-ziibiing, gagwe-gikendang gegoo ji-wiindamaagowizid. Ezhi-bazangwaabid gagwe-bagakendang. Nishikewinaagoz, gaawiin dash wiin eta namadabisii. Nenaboozhoon obii-gii-mooji-ganoonigoon.

Ezhi-bazigwiid onaanaagadawaaban-daan gidakiimanaan. Ezhi-odaapinang ashkaadigoowadikwan ezhi-waawiyeyaaginang omakazineyaabi odakobijigaagen. Ezhi-agoodood imaa nookweziganimitigoonsing.

Ezhi-waabamaad asabikeshiinh mindimooyenhyan bimookiinid imaa mashkosiikaang ezhi-akwaandawaadang waakaayaa-gibijigan. Weweni go ani-akwaandaweyode. Ezhi-maajii-gaganoonigod.

"Grandson, you know my voice. You and your people heard me when I told you to look to the Seven Sacred Directions for my Teachings. You heard, you listened and all was good.

"But lately, you have been hearing other voices." The Elder Spider spun her web as she spoke.

"You are hearing voices that are not mine. Now is the time for you to rely on the wisdom you learned from Amik. Use that wisdom to distinguish these voices from mine. Look to Makwa for the courage you will need to resist them. What goes up – will come down. For every right, there is a wrong. For each of my Teachings – there is a Deceiver. These voices are those of Seven Deceivers."

"Noozhis, gigikenim eni-taagoziyaan. Giinawaa aazha gigii-noondawim gaa-gii-izhi-wiindamawinagook ji-inaabiyeg ezhi-niizhwaaswi-gagiikwewinan. Gigii-noondaam, gigii-pizindaam gakina gegoo gii-minose.

"Ingodig idash bakaan gegoo gidizhi-noondaanaawaa." Mindimooyenh-asabikeshiinhnh ezhi-maajii-asabiked.

"Bakaan awiya ginoondawaawaag, gaawiin niin gaa-ikidowaan. Mii sa zhigwa-ji-naanaagazotawegoban ezhi-gikendaasod awe Amik. Mii iwe ge-bizindamegoban weweni ji-naanaagadawendimeg gaa-gii-ininigog. Naanaagadawenim Makwa ge-onji-mashkowendameg ji-gwayakwendameg. Gaa-ishpiseg daa-biniisikaa. Endaso-debwewin, maji-ikidowin. Ezhi-gagiikweyaan, awiya oga-gagwe-niisibidoon."

EAST • WAABANONG

On a fine, silky thread, Trickster lowered herself toward the center of the hoop. With her gaze fixed on the young man, she spun, moving Eastward.

"Start every day under Father Sky looking East, up at your Grandfather, the Sun. Is he not majestic and powerful? Do you need more than that to remind you how small and pitiful you are? Did I not tell you to look to Wolf as the example of my first Teaching, that of Humility?

"Yet you hear a voice telling you that you are better than others. This voice is telling you that you should stand tall and proud and let others know how good and special you are. That voice you are hearing is that of Pride. Pride teases and intrigues you. Pride would have you believe that you are better than your neighbour. Pride would have you impose your views and values on that neighbour. Pride would have you make war against him. Grandson, being proud of who you are is not wrong, but understand that you are no better than others. You are all equal in the eyes of Creator.

Iniwe odasabikaanan, mii dash imaa gaa-izhi-bida'ogod endasabikaaning. Ezhi-naanaagadawaabamaad oshki-ininiwan, gaa-ani-izhi-inoodebatood waabanong.

"Endaso gigizheb waabangong inaabin, ganawaabam gimishoomisinaan giizis. Inashkwe epiichi-mashkawinaagosid. Naawaj ina geyaabi gegoo ginandawendaan epiichi-goopazinaagoziyan? Aanawi gosha gigii-wiidamawin ji-naanaagadawaabamad Ma'iingan ji-mikwendaman nitam-gaa-gii-izhi-gikino'amawinaan?

"Bakaan awiya ginoondawaag naawaj giin epiichi-mashkawenimoyan. Ogowe gaa-noondawodwaa gii-kakwe-wanashkwemigoog anishaa gidigoog. Mamekwaazowin inendaman naawaj niin nimashkawendam apiich idash giin. Mamekwaazowin gigaa-miigaanigon. Noozhis, gaawiin ningodino mashkawenidinzoyan, gidaa-gikendam gaawiin giin awashime gidaawisii. Gakina naasaab gidaawimin ezhi-naanaagandawaabaminang gimanidoominaan.

"Do not listen to Pride. Do not allow it into your heart. Look instead to Wolf, to Ma'iigan. Be humble. Do as he does. Bow your head in reverence to your Creator, to your Elders and to those who are weaker than you, to those who have less than you. Live by my Teachings and all will be good."

"Gego bazindangen Mamekwaazowin. Gego giga-wanimigoosii. Naawaj gidaa-ganawaabamaa Ma'iingan. Gidimaagenidizon. Izhichigen ezhichiged. Nawagikwetow gigitiziimag, gimanidoom gaye gaa-zhaagwaadiziwaad gaa-gidimaagiziwaad. Ganawendan ningagiikwewinan mii'i ge-izhi-minoseg."

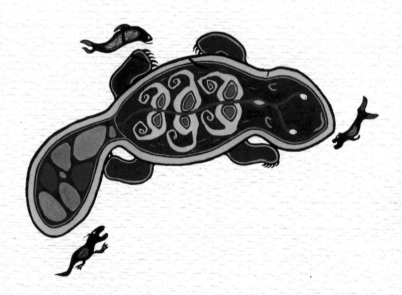

SOUTH • ZHAAWANONG

Grandmother Spider continued spinning, moving Southward.

"When you travel South, you will be in the prime of your life. You will be strong, capable and wanting to achieve great things. On occasion, you will want for that which is not yours. Your desire will be so strong that you will lie, cheat and cause hurt.

"The voice that you will be hearing is that of Lust. Lust will drive you to want so badly that it will drive you insane to the point of doing things you would not otherwise do. Do not listen to Lust. Be honest with yourself about what you have and about what you need.

"Look to Raven, Gaagáági, who succeeds and thrives with what he has been given. He is bright, alert and always conscious of the gift Creator has given him. He does not lust for that which is not his. Nor should you.

"Be honest with others and with yourself. Do not lie, cheat or steal. Know that you have enough. Be satisfied. Then, be thankful. Offer Tobacco in thanks."

Mindimooyenh-asabikiisii geyaabi asabike, zhaawanong ani-izhaad.

"Zhaawanong ani-izhaayan giga-mashkowendam. Giga-mashkowendam geyaabi gegoo ji-debinaman ezhi-andone'igeyan. Ingoding giga-ondawendaan gaawiin dash giin iwe gidoodaya'iimisiin. Aapachi dash giga-misawendaan giga-gagiinawishk giga-maashidoodawaag giji-bimaadiziig.

"Ezhi-noondaman noojiikaazowin. Noojiikaazowin giga-zhaagooji'igon giga-giiwashkweyendam giga-maazhidoodam gaawiin wiikaa gaa-gii-toodaziiyamban. Gego bizindangen noojiikendamowin. Naanaagadawendan minik gegaa aazha gaa-ayaayan.

"Naanaagadawaabam Gaagaagi ogichi-apiitendaan omiinigoowiziwin. Aapachi bagakendam gaa-izhi-miinigoowizid. Gaawiin awashime gegoo onandawendanziin. Gaawiin gegiin iwe gida-inendazii.

"Weweni gwayakwenindizon gaye giiji-bimaadiziig. Gego gagiinawishkiken gaye gimoodiken. Na'endan minik gegoo eyaayan. Gaye gidaa-biindaakoojige ji-miigwechiwitaagoziyan."

WEST • NINGAABII'ANONG

Trickster inched her way Westward.

"You are hearing the voice of another ... the cousin of the Deceiver Lust. Beware of this one. Beware of Envy.

"When you travel West on your journey through life, you will have achieved much. You will be happy with who you are because you will be humble and you will be honest with yourself. You will have recognized the gift you have been given and you will have achieved much. On your journey, you will have seen many who are smaller and weaker than you. Yet there will be things they possess that you were not given. Do not envy others. You have enough.

"Buffalo is the largest and the strongest among you. Buffalo offers himself to you so that you might survive. Do you envy his strength and beauty? Do you think Buffalo is less worthy than you? Do you think Creator favours you over him? Of course you don't. You understand that he is your equal. You understand that you are related ... you are all related.

"Did I not teach you that when hunting Buffalo, you should take only what you need? Did I not teach you not to waste? Show him respect by leaving Tobacco and by not wasting. This is good. This is right. This is respectful.

"Grandson, look to the West and remember this Teaching. Shut out the voice of Envy."

Asabikeshiinh-mindimooyenh ningaabii'anong gii-ani-izhaa.

"Miinawaa awiya ginoondawaa ... owiijii'aaganan gaa-maji-naanaagadawendaminid. nisiditaw gawondenigeshkid.

"Ningaabii'anong ani-izhaayan, niibowa gegoo giga-ani-mikaan. Giga-minwendam awenen ayaawiyan giga-debwewenindiz. Giga-nisidotaanan gimiinigowiziwinan. Niibowa gigii-waabamaag naawaji wiinawaa ge-dimaagiziwaad naawaji dash giin. Minikegoo gaa-gii-kashkitoowaad, gego ondenimaaken. Aazha giin gidebise.

"Mashkodebizhiki mindido mashkawaadizi gaye. Idash gidaazhawinimaag ge-onji-mino-bimaadiziyan. Gidoondenimaa na ezhi-mashkawaadizid gaye ezhi-mino-naagozid? Gimajenimaa na apiichi dash giin? Naawaj niin ningichi-apiitendaagoz gidinendam ina? Gaawiin gosha. Gidaa-gikendaan daabidawendaagoziyeg gidinawendim gosha.

"Digo dash gigii-kino'mawind gii-andawenjigeyan, minik eta go ezhi-andawendimanitoon. Gego gegoo webinagen. Gidaa-biindaakoonaa epiitenimad. Mii owe minochigewin.

"Noozhis inaabin ningaabii'anong minjimendan gaa-giikwewinan. Gego bizindangen Aazhendamowin?"

13

NORTH • GIIWEDINONG

"Can you imagine the destruction Makwa could cause if she chose violence, aggression and Wrath as her guides? She does not. Bear has the Courage to suppress the voice of the Deceiver Wrath and so must you.

"By the time you move North in your journey, you will have learned from Wolf, Raven and Buffalo. You will understand what you have been given. You will have been grateful and you will have lived your life based on that gift. The landscape you now find yourself on will be white. Your hair will be white. You will have known pain and pleasure and you will have seen much wrong … much that angers you.

"Grandson, even with all you have learned, it is not for you to pass judgment. Yes, you will see wrong that causes suffering and hurt and yes, you could respond with violence and Wrath. But it is not for you to do so. Be courageous enough to accept that all of Creator's children are on a different journey. They too are learning. Be strong enough to accept this truth. Look to Makwa for strength and courage. Listen to her. Do not follow the lead of Wrath."

"Gidaa-mikwendaan giishpin Makwa nishkaadendang minik gegoo ge-izhi-maazhichigepan? Gaawiin dash i'i inaadizisii. Gaawiin obinzidanziin Aazhendamowin, gegiin sa gidaa-izhichige.

"Zhigwa giiwedinong ge-ani-izhaayan, gigii-kikinoo'amaagoog Ma'iingan, Gaagaagi, Makwa gaye. Giga-nisidawinaan gimiinigoziwin. Giga-miigwechiwendaanan gimiinigoowiziwinan mii dash owe gwayak ge-izhi-bimaadiyan. Gidakiiminaan da-waabishkiinaagwad dibishkoo go gii-nizisan. Gigii-kikendaan maanendamowin gaye minowaanigoziwin gigiiwaabandaan gaa-onji-nishkaadendaman.

"Noozhis, gego anawaabamaaken awiya misawaago aanawi niibowa gegoo gaa-izhi-gimiinigoowiziiyan. Eya' geget giga-waabandaan maazhichigewin, giga-nishkaadendamose dash, idash giin gaawiin gegoo gidaa-izhichigesii. Gagwe-mashkawendan ji-gikendaman bebakaan gakina awiya inaadizi. Gewiinawaa ondawenjigewag. Mikwenim Makwa gaa-gii-izhi-gikinoo'mawig. Bizindaw. Gego bishigwa'adooken."

FATHER SKY • GIIWEDINONG

"There is another among them, one whose name is Sloth.

"Sloth would lead you down the path of comfort and laziness. Sloth will tell you to lie back, relax and do little with the gift you have been given. Shut him out.

"Look toward Father Sky and think of Amik. Learn from Beaver. Few work as hard as Beaver does and none understand the way Beaver understands that if she does not use the gift Creator has given her, she will die. Beaver must work her teeth constantly or they will grow through and she will die. Yes, she works hard, but she also has the wisdom to use her gift. So must you. Use your gift. Learn from Amik and shut out the voice of the Deceiver Sloth."

"Bezhig miinawaa awiya ge-timishkid izhinikaazo.

"Apane go gagwe-anwebi ezhi-gitimid. Gidaa-gwashkwaawaajishin gego memwech babaamendangen gimiinigoowiziwinan. Gego bizindawaaken. Inaabin giizhigong naanaagadawenim Amik. Waabam ezhichiged Amik. Aanind eta go awiya enigok anokiiwag. Gaawiin igo awiya onisidawinaaziinaawaa wegonen apane wenji-gichi-anookiid Amik. Giishpin anokaadansig omiinigoowisiwinan, gaawiin da-mino-bimaadizisii.

"Apane go odaabajitoonan wiibidan ji-maajii-gizininik, da-ganawaadamwaapineshin. Eya' apane gichi-anokii weweni odaabajitoon gaa-izhi-miinigoowisid. Gegiin i'i gidaa-izhichige. Ganawaabam Amik ezhichiged gego bizindiwaaken gaa-kitimishkid."

MOTHER EARTH • GIGICHI-OMAAMAANAAN

Trickster's web appeared finished yet she went on.

"Grandson, look down at Mother Earth. Look at her and listen to her heartbeat. Is it not the beat you hear in your own heart? It is not surprising. You are from her. You came from her and you will return to her. She feeds and she clothes and she protects you. She provides you with everything you need and more. She is there for you to use – not to abuse.

"There is one who would have you take and take and take some more. Take of your mother, yes ... but always put back that which you do not use. Always replace that which you have taken. If you do not, there will be nothing left for your children. Your mother has much to give you yet when it is gone, it is gone for all time. This is true. Learn this truth and live by it.

"Look at Turtle as she moves slowly across the breast of Mother Earth. Think of Mother Earth as Turtle Island. Know that she has limits. Do not strip your Mother bare of all she has. Do not deface or abuse her or soil her beauty. She has given you all she can and all she is. Use her wisely as you use the gift you have been given. Balance. Courage. Wisdom and Truth. Gluttony has no limits and no place in your heart."

Waabamaan asabikeshiinhwasabiin gigiishichigaazonid mindimooyenh-asabikeshiinh miinawaa maaji-gaagiigido.

"Noozhis, ganawaabam gigichi-maa-maanaan. Bizindan gide' baga'ang. Mii gosha iwe ga-noondaman gide' baga'ang. Gaawiin gidaa-goshkwendanzii mii gosha imaa gaa-poonji'ayaayan mii gaye imaa ge-izhi-azhegiiweyan. Gidashamig gibiichikonaye'ig giganawenimig. Akina gegoo gimiinig ezhi-anda-wendaman booshke nawaaj geyaabi. Mii awe gaa-wiiji'ig gego maazhidoodawaaken.

"Aanind awiya gego apane gaa-odaa-pinamowaad gego gikinawaabamaaken. Naanaagadawenim gimaamaanaan, azhewitoon gegoo gaa-andawendan-ziwan. Giishpin izhichigesiwan gaawiin gegoo ginagadamawaasiig giniijaanisag. Niibowaa gegoo gimiinigonaan gimaa-maanaa, giishpin gegoo azhetoosiwan gaawiin geyaabi gegoo gigawaabandan-ziin. Debwewin o'owe. Inaadiziwin o'owe.

"Naanaagandawaabam Mikinaak ezhi-besikaad. Ganawaabam Gimaamaanaan Mikinaakominisiwid. Gidaa-gikendaan minik gegoo gii-odaapinaman gego mash-ashkobinaaken. Apane go niibowaa gegoo giwiiji'ig gaye enaadizid. Weweni nisidotaw dibishkoo go gimiinigoowinan. Debwew-in, minosewin, zoongenimowin debwew-endamowin. Aanind awiya, gaawiin giken-danziin ji-gibijiid gegoo gii-odaabanang."

19

WITHIN • IZHIMAAMAWI

The wise, old Spider hung motionless
in the center of the hoop, suspended by
a single thread.

"Of the Seven Deceivers, Greed is the
most dangerous and the most alluring.
Grandson, you must fight Greed with
all your heart. Your journey along the
Good Red Road should be one of giving,
not taking. This is love. Only when you
are honest about what you have
and about who you are; only when
you are satisfied with your gift and
respectful of others … only then will
you be capable of loving yourself
and then, loving others.

"Fight greed with love. Look to Eagle.
She is there, high in the sky close
to Creator. Look within yourself …
into your heart. Eagle will be there
and so will I."

Mindimooyenh-asabikeshiinh
goshkwaawaadigooshin odasabiing.

"Ezhi-niizhwaachiwaad gaa-
kagwe-maazhichigewaad, awe
gaa-kaazhage'endang aapachi go
naniizaanendaagozi. Noozhis, gego
giga-zhaagooji'igosii gaa-kaazhiged.
Mino-bimaadiziwin bima'adooyan
misko-miikana azhewitoon gegoo
bangii eta gegoo odaapinan. Mii
owe gizhewaadiziwin. Weweni
naanaagajitooyan enaadiziyan:
epiitendaman gimiinigooziwinan,
maanaaji'adwaa giiji-bimaadiziig …
mii'i gii-oditaman epiitenidizoyan gaye
giiji-bimaadiziig.

"Gizhewaadiziwin apane
minjimendan. Inashke ganwaabam
Migizi. Waasa ishpimiing
babaamaashi obeshwanji'aan
Gigichi-gimishoomisinaanin.
Naanaagadawaabandizon giwaabamig
gimishoomishinaan geniin sa go."

21

"Grandson, take this hoop back to your village. Hang it near your resting place. I gift it to you.

"My webbing will entrap those voices that are not mine.

"I have left an opening here in the center to allow my voice to find its way through to your heart."

Pointing at the young man's heart, Trickster lowered herself to the ground and quickly vanished into the sage brush.

"Noozhis, anigiiwewish wa'awe asabiins. Jiigishkwaand izhi-agoozh. Mii iwe gaa-miininaan. Asabiinsing da-bida'ogoowag gaa-kagwe-zhaagozimikwaa. Naawisabiins giga-onji-noondaw gaganooninaan."

Asabikeshiinh odizhinoo'waan ode'ining, gaa-ani-izhi-maajii-odebatood noopiing.

23

At the end of the fourth day of his Vision Quest, a young Anishinabek man stood by his village council fire sharing a story.

In his hands, he held a webbed hoop, the sacred gift to be used and shared by all of Breath Giver's children.

Eko-niiyogon-nagadanig, gwiiwizens ogii-okwabi'aa' jiigeweshkode, ogii-tadibwaajimotawa'.

Odakonaan asabikeshiinhwasabiisan, mii owe omiigiwewin gimishoomisinaan gakina wiiya ji-aabajitood ge-onji-mino-bimaadizid.

24

For the students, staff and parents of David Bouchard Public School. Thank you for honouring me. Thank you for including me in your dreams. Might I somehow learn to live up to what you see in me . . . — D.B.

To my family, Mike, Kelly, Emlyn, and Keira — for keeping me in the present while I dream of the past; to Annie Wilson for dreaming my name, Wasageeghegook; and to Willie Wilson for your teachings. — K.C.

For my family — my wife Marie, and children Kyla, Daylyn, and Keenan — and especially for my grandchildren Maslyn, Tydzeh, Sadeya and Ry'den, who are the most passionate lovers of my music. — S.K.

Copyright © 2013 David Bouchard
Art copyright © 2013 Kristy Cameron
Art on title page and page 4 © 2013 Kelly Duquette
Music copyright © 2013 Stephen Kakfwi
Published in Canada in 2013
7 6 5 4 3 2 1

LIBRARY AND ARCHIVES CANADA CATALOGUING IN PUBLICATION
Bouchard, David, 1952–

Dreamcatcher and the seven deceivers = Asabikeshiiwasp gaye awiya
oga-gagwe-niisibidoon / David Bouchard ; paintings by Kristy Cameron ;
music by Stephen Kakfwi ; Ojibwe language by Jason & Nancy Jones.
Issued also in French under title: Le capteur de rêves et les sept tentations.
Text in English and Ojibwa.
ISBN 978-0-9784327-9-9

1. Indians of North America—Religion. 2. Deadly sins. I. Cameron, Kristy, 1968–
II. Kakfwi, Stephen III. Jones, Jason, 1980– IV. Jones, Nancy, 1939– V. Title.
VI. Title: Asabikeshiiwasp gaye awiya oga-gagwe-niisibidoon.
E98.R3B66 2013   299.7'122   C2013-901746-1

More Than Words Publishers
823 Hendecourt Road, North Vancouver, BC V7K 2X5
604-985-2527
www.MTWPublishers.com

Art on title page and page 4 by Kelly Duquette
Ojibwe translation by Jason & Nancy Jones; reading by Jason Jones
Flute music by David Bouchard; played on Swampfox Flutes | http://swampfoxflutes.com/
Copy edited by Bonnie Chapman & Jocelyn Rea
Book design by Arifin Graham, Alaris Design
Sound Design and Mastering by Geoff Edwards at streamworks.ca
Special thanks to Michael Cameron Photography and Gerhard Aichelberger,
    PrintSmith Group
Produced by Chris Patrick
Printed and bound in Canada by Friesens on 100% pcw recycled paper

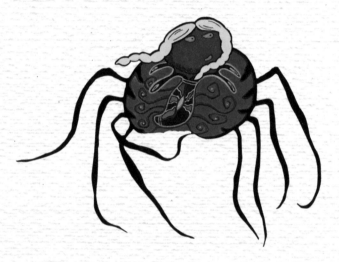